GARDEN WILDLIFE STICKER BOOK

Phillip Clarke

Illustrated by Trevor Boyer, Phil Weare and Denise Finney

Designed by Karen Tomlins
Additional designs by Michael Hill

Edited by Kirsteen Rogers

Consultant: Dr Margaret Rostron

How to use this book

There are over a hundred different animals in this book. Using the descriptions and pictures, try to match each sticker to the right entry. If you need help, an index and checklist at the back of the book tells you which sticker goes with which animal. You can also use this book as a spotter's handbook to make a note of the creatures you have seen. At the back of the book, there's also a list of words you may not know.

The measurements given for the animals are all averages.
The pictures below show how the different types of animal are measured:

In this book you will find these signs: ♀ means the animal is female ♂ means the animal is male

Birds: length from beak to tip of tail

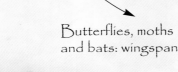

Butterflies, moths and bats: wingspan

Snails: length of shell

Spiders: body length, not including legs

Other insects: body length, not including feelers

Mammals and amphibians: head and body length, not including tail

Other creepy-crawlies: body length

Small birds

Many of the birds in this book live in gardens, and can be seen all year round. A few are seasonal visitors from abroad.

Great tit

Blue tit

Blue tit

Length: 11cm (4¼in)

Blue tits can be spotted climbing on garden bird-feeders. They have bright yellow breasts and blue feathers on their wings and heads. Their faces are white with a black stripe across each eye.

WHEN ....

WHERE ....

Great tit

Length: 14cm (5½in)

This is the largest tit found in Europe. It has a black head with white cheeks, and a black stripe down the middle of its yellow breast. Its wings are dark bluish-grey.

WHEN ....

WHERE ....

Long-tailed tit (Britain and western Europe)

Long-tailed tit (northern and eastern Europe)

Long-tailed tit

Length: 14cm (5½in)

These fluffy, rounded birds are easily recognized by their long, tapering, black and white tails. They often feed in flocks of about a dozen, near the treetops, but they build their nests in bushes.

WHEN ....

WHERE ....

Greenfinch

Length: 15cm (6in)

Greenfinches have stout beaks, which they use to crack open large seeds. They are mossy green, with grey and yellow markings on their wings and tails. The males are more brightly coloured than the females.

WHEN ....

WHERE ....

Greenfinch

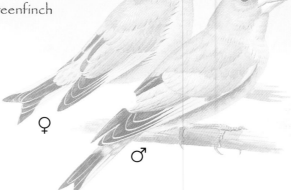

♀

♂

Chaffinch

Length: 15cm (6in)

Chaffinches are often seen in gardens. The male has a pink breast and face, a grey head and two white bars on its wings. The female is pale brown with white wing bars.

WHEN ....

WHERE ....

Chaffinch

Siskin

Length: 11cm (4¼in)

Large numbers of these little finches visit western and southern Europe in winter. They have black and yellow tails and wings, and yellow rumps. Males have black foreheads. Siskins nest in conifer woods, and may visit gardens for peanuts.

WHEN ....

WHERE ....

Siskin

Goldfinch

Bullfinch

Length: 15cm (6in)

Bullfinches have rounded bodies and large heads with black faces and "caps". Their wings are grey and black with a white stripe. The male has a pink breast; the female's is brown.

WHEN ....

WHERE ....

Brambling

Length: 15cm (6in)

These finches have orange breasts with white bellies and rumps. They travel south from northern Europe in winter. Then, the males' heads are brown, but they are usually glossy black. Bramblings feed in flocks on grain and beechnuts.

WHEN ....

WHERE ....

Goldfinch

Length: 12cm (4¾in)

This little finch is brown, with a red, white and black face and a yellow bar on its wings. It feeds on the seeds of thistles and teasels.

WHEN ....

WHERE ....

Bullfinch

Brambling

Other small birds

House sparrow

Length: 17cm (6¾in)

House sparrows are a familiar sight, as they live near people and eat their scraps. They are brown with black streaks and grey undersides. The male has a black face and throat, and the top of its head is grey.

WHEN ....

WHERE ....

Tree sparrow

House sparrow

♂

♀

Dunnock

Length: 14.5cm (5¾in)

Also called a hedge sparrow, this common bird is usually seen shuffling near undergrowth. It has a brown, stripy back, a bluish-grey head and neck, and a paler underside. Its beak is short and it has large feet.

WHEN ....

WHERE ....

Dunnock

Tree sparrow

Length: 14cm (5½in)

Both sexes of this little sparrow look similar: brown on the top of the head and neck with a black smudge on the cheek. They usually nest in holes in trees or cliffs, but will use garden nest-boxes.

WHEN ....

WHERE ....

Nuthatch

Length: 14cm (5½in)

This chubby bird may be seen walking headfirst down the trunks of old trees. It has a golden-brown breast, greyish-blue wings and a thick, black stripe across each eye. It has a very short tail and a pointed beak.

WHEN ....

WHERE ....

Wren

Wren

Length: 9.5cm (3¾in)

The song of this common, tiny bird is surprisingly loud. It has a short, round body, short wings and a pointed beak. Its feathers are speckled brown.

WHEN ....

WHERE ....

Nuthatch

Robin

Robin

Length: 14cm (5½in)

Robins have brick-red breasts, and brown wings and backs. They sing through the winter and, if they're near street lights, even at night.

WHEN ....

WHERE ....

Pied wagtail

Blackcap

Length: 14cm (5½in)

Blackcaps can often be seen in trees, moving from perch to perch as they sing. The males have a black "cap" on their heads. The female's is reddish-brown.

WHEN ....

WHERE ....

Pied wagtail and white wagtail

Length: 18cm (7in)

White wagtail

Pied wagtails are common in Britain, and white wagtails are more often seen in Europe. Wagtails are so named because they're always wagging their tails up and down.

WHEN ....

WHERE ....

Blackcap

♂

♀

♂

♀

Linnet

Spotted flycatcher

Length: 14cm (5½in)

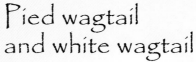
Spotted flycatcher

You may spot this bird perching in the open, near trees, as it watches out for insects to snap up with its longish beak. It has a pale, streaked breast and head, with a little crest. Its tail and wings are long.

WHEN ....

WHERE ....

Linnet

Length: 13cm (5in)

These slim finches have short, grey beaks and brown backs. The male has a grey head, and, in summer, a red breast and forehead. Linnets nest in bushes, especially gorse, and feed on the seeds of weeds.

WHEN ....

WHERE ....

Medium-sized birds

Song thrush

Length: 23cm (9in)

Song thrushes have black-speckled fronts and are rust-coloured under their wings. They are often seen near trees or bushes, or breaking open snail shells by smashing them against a stone.

WHEN ....

WHERE ....

Song thrush

Blackbird

♀

♂

Blackbird

Length: 25cm (9¾in)

This member of the thrush family is often seen in gardens. The male is black with a bright yellow beak. The female is dark brown with a slightly speckled breast and a duller beak.

WHEN ....

WHERE ....

Juvenile (young) starling

Adult starling (winter)

Starling

Length: 22cm (8¾in)

Starlings have blackish-brown feathers with a glossy, green and purple sheen, and white speckles in winter. They often gather in large flocks.

WHEN ....

WHERE ....

Jay

Mistle thrush

Length: 27cm (10¾in)

Bigger, paler and more upright than song thrushes, mistle thrushes are white under their wings. They often perch in treetops to sing, even in bad weather. Their food includes worms and berries.

WHEN ....

WHERE ....

Mistle thrush

Jay

Length: 32cm (12½in)

This pinkish-brown bird is a member of the crow family. It has pale blue shoulder patches and a black "moustache". Jays often hide in trees, but you may hear their harsh, screeching call.

WHEN ....

WHERE ....

Swift

Length: 17cm (6¾in)

Swifts are often found in small flocks and are fast, skilful fliers that can even sleep in the air. These dark brown birds have short necks and short, forked tails, but their wings are very long and pointed.

WHEN ....

WHERE ....

Swallow

Swift

Swallow

Length: 19cm (7½in)

Swallows have very long, forked tails. They have blue-black backs with red markings on their faces, and are white underneath.

WHEN ....

WHERE ....

House martin

Length: 13cm (5in)

House martins are small and dark blue with a large, white patch across the rump. They are snow-white underneath, and have short, forked tails.

WHEN ....

WHERE ....

House martin

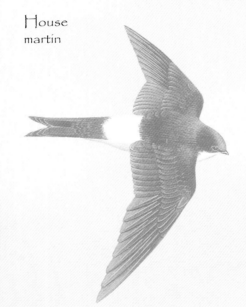

Great spotted woodpecker

Length: 23cm (9in)

In spring, this woodpecker may be heard drumming on trees with its beak. It has a white breast and a black and white body, with red marks under its tail. The male has a red patch on the back of its head.

WHEN ....

WHERE ....

Green woodpecker

♂

Green woodpecker

Length: 32cm (12½in)

Green woodpeckers are often seen on the ground, hunting for ants. They have green wings and backs, with paler underparts, a yellow rump, a red "cap", and red and black face-markings (just black on the female). Their call sounds like a loud laugh.

WHEN ....

WHERE ....

♂

Great spotted woodpecker

7

Medium-sized and large birds

Rock dove and town pigeon

Length: 33cm (13in)

Town pigeons are descended from rock doves, which live in small groups on sea cliffs. Rock doves are dark and light grey, with slightly pink breasts and dark, stripy markings on their wings. Their legs are pink. Town pigeons can be many different colours.

WHEN ....

WHERE ....

Town pigeons

Rock dove

Woodpigeon

Length: 41cm (16in)

Woodpigeon

These large pigeons are common in all areas with trees. They are grey with a pinkish-brown breast and white patches on their neck.

WHEN ....

WHERE ....

Collared dove

Length: 30cm (11¾in)

This pale, slender dove has a black and white "collar" on the back of its neck. Usually seen alone, or in pairs, it feeds mainly on grain. Its call is "coo cooo coo".

WHEN ....

WHERE ....

Collared dove

♂

Sparrowhawk

Sparrowhawk

Length: Female 38cm (15in)
Male 30cm (11¾in)

Sparrowhawks hunt other birds. The male has a bluish-grey back and wings, and a striped underside. Its grey tail has four or five dark bars. The female is larger and browner. Both have yellow feet.

WHEN ....

WHERE ....

Tawny owl

Tawny owl

Length: 38cm (15in)

This plump, speckled-brown owl has a large, round head and big, black eyes. Tawny owls nest in holes in old trees. The males call, "whoo, tu-whoo", and the females answer, "tu-whit".

WHEN ....

WHERE ....

Carrion crow and hooded crow

Length: 47cm (18½in)

Hooded crows have pale grey bodies with black wings and heads, while carrion crows are all black. Both have large, strong beaks and eat many things, including birds' eggs and carrion (dead meat).

WHEN ....

WHERE ....

Carrion crow

Hooded crow

Jackdaw

Jackdaw

Length: 33cm (13in)

Jackdaws can be told from other crows by the pale grey on the back and sides of their head, their grey eyes, and shorter beaks. They live by old trees and buildings, and also near cliffs. Flocks of jackdaws often feed together.

WHEN ....

WHERE ....

Grey heron

Length: 92cm (36¼in)

Herons sometimes land in gardens to take fish from ponds. They have grey and white bodies, with long necks and legs. They have black eye-stripes and a black tuft on the back of their head.

WHEN ....

WHERE ....

Grey heron

Magpie

White stork

Magpie

Length: 46cm (18in)

This common bird is black with white patches on its sides. It has a long tail which gleams with blue, green and purple in certain lights.

WHEN ....

WHERE ....

White stork

Length: 102cm (40in)

Not often seen in Britain, this huge, white bird has black wing feathers, a long, red beak and long, red legs. Storks often build big nests on rooftops or telegraph poles.

WHEN ....

WHERE ....

Creepy-crawlies

Insects have six legs, but some creepy-crawlies, for example millipedes, have many more. Others, such as slugs and snails, slither along on a single "foot".

Garden snail

Length: 25–35mm (1–1½in)

These common snails have grey bodies and large, rounded yellow-brown shells with dark bands. They hide under stones in the day, coming out at night to feed on plants.

WHEN ....

WHERE ....

Garden snail

Garden slug

Length: 25–30mm (1–1¼in)

This yellowish-grey slug has black stripes on its sides, and an orangey underside. It leaves a yellow trail of slime as it moves. Slugs spend the day in damp, shady places, emerging at night, or after rain.

WHEN ....

WHERE ....

Garden slug

Netted slug

Length: 35mm (1½in)

The body of this very common slug is yellowish, mottled with darker markings. It leaves a white, slimy trail. Its taste for fruit, leaves and plant roots makes it very unpopular with gardeners.

WHEN ....

WHERE ....

Netted slug

Garden spider

Length: 7–18mm (¼–¾in)

This yellow-brown spider can be recognized by the cross-shaped pattern of white spots on its back. It spins a sticky web to catch flying insects, and often hangs, head-down, at its centre.

WHEN ....

WHERE ....

Garden spider

Earthworm

Length: 10–30cm (4–11¾in)

Often seen above the soil after rain, this worm has a pointed, brownish-red front end and a pale back end, with a "saddle" in between. It tunnels underground, eating dead plant matter, and plugs the end of its burrow with leaves.

WHEN ....

WHERE ....

Saddle

Earthworm

Snake millipede

Length: 20–30mm (¾–1¼in)

These creatures have tube-shaped bodies
and about 100 legs. Active at night, they
feed on rotten wood and plant roots. Snake
millipedes coil up if they are disturbed.

WHEN ....

WHERE ....

Snake
millipede

Common shiny woodlouse

Length: 15–18mm (½–¾in)

Woodlice live in damp places and feed on dead plants
and rotting wood. This type has a flattish, shiny,
brown-black body with pale edges. Unlike some
woodlice, it can't roll up into a ball to
protect itself.

WHEN ....

WHERE ....

Common shiny
woodlouse

Common earwig

Length: 15mm (½in)

Common earwigs are brown, and have tiny wing
cases and long rear-ends with pincers. When
they feel threatened, they spread and raise their
pincers. They can fly, but don't often do so.

WHEN ....

WHERE ....

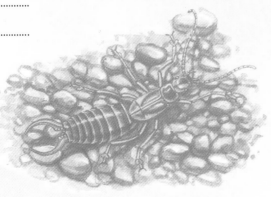

Common
earwig

Centipede

Centipede

Length: 18–30mm (¾–1¼in)

Centipedes have long, segmented, shiny,
chestnut brown bodies and 30 legs. They
live in damp, dark places, such as under
stones, or in cellars. They poison and kill
insects and slugs with their front claws.

WHEN ....

WHERE ....

House cricket

House cricket

Length: 16mm (¾in)

You may hear a house cricket's shrill
song in and around heated buildings
and greenhouses in winter. They are
also found in rubbish heaps.

WHEN ....

WHERE ....

Butterflies

Butterflies lay their eggs on particular plants, known as their food plants. After their caterpillars hatch, feeding on these plants gives them the energy they need to change into adult butterflies.

Common blue

Holly blue

Wingspan: 26–34mm (1–1¼in)

In spring, these pale blue butterflies are seen on holly bushes, where they lay their eggs. The females have broad black borders to their front wings; males have narrower borders.

WHEN ....

WHERE ....

Holly blue

♀ ♀

♂ ♂

Common blue

Wingspan: 28–36mm (1–1½in)

As its name suggests, this butterfly is common throughout Europe. It is found in grassy, flowery places. The male is blue, and the female brown (or bluish-brown) with orange marks near the wing edges.

WHEN ....

WHERE ....

Small white

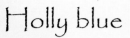

♀ ♂

♂ ♀

Small white

Wingspan: 48–50mm (about 2in)

Small white butterflies are often called cabbage whites as they are often seen near cabbages, where they lay their eggs. Look for the black tips on small whites' front wings. The female has two black marks on each front wing; the male has one.

WHEN ....

WHERE ....

Meadow brown

Wingspan: 50–55mm (2–2¼in)

This common butterfly is found throughout Europe. You can spot it flitting over meadows and grassy areas, even when it's raining. Look out for a black eye-spot with a white centre on each front wing.

WHEN ....

WHERE ....

♂

♀

Meadow brown

♀ ♂

14

15

16

17

Cutworm

18

19

20

21

22

23

24

25

♀

♂

26

27   28

29

30

Gills

31

32

33

34

35

36

37

38

39   40   41

56

57

58

59

60

61

62

63

64

65

66

67

68

69

70

71

♀ ♂ ♀

♂

72

♀ ♀

♂ ♂

73

74

75

76

77

♀

♂

78

79

80

81

♂

♀

♀ ♂

82

83

84

85

86

87

88

89

90

♀ ♂

91

92 ♂

93

94

95

96

97

98

99

100

♂
♀

101
♂

102

103

104

105

106

107

108

109

110

111

112

113
♀
♂

Peacock

Wingspan: 62–68mm (2½–2¾in)

In most of Europe, this gorgeous butterfly is usually seen visiting flowers in gardens and orchards. It has bright eye-spots on its wings, like a peacock's tail.

WHEN ....

WHERE ....

Peacock

Small tortoiseshell

Wingspan: 48–52mm (about 2in)

Small tortoiseshells are found in flowery places all over Europe. Look for the blue half-moon markings along the edges of their brightly patterned wings.

WHEN ....

WHERE ....

Small tortoiseshell

♀ ♂
Orange tip

Orange tip

Wingspan: 42–48mm (1¾–2in)

You can easily recognize this pretty butterfly by the orange tips on the male's front wings. It is found in hedgerows, woods and flowery meadows in most European countries.

WHEN ....

WHERE ....

Painted lady

Painted lady

Wingspan: 62–65mm (about 2½in)

This black and orange garden butterfly visits Europe from north Africa, and lays its eggs on thistles. Look out for the white blobs on its front wings. You will see more painted ladies in some years than others.

WHEN ....

WHERE ....

Red admiral

Wingspan: 66–68mm (2½–2¾in)

Red admirals are common in gardens throughout Europe. They are black with red bands and white spots on their front wings. Unlike other butterflies, they sometimes fly at night.

WHEN ....

WHERE ....

Red admiral

Moths

Most moths fly at night-time, and are usually seen on warm, overcast nights. They are often attracted to lights.

Garden tiger

Large yellow underwing

Wingspan: 45–60mm (1¾–2¼in)

This common moth sometimes flies into houses at night. Its back wings are yellow with black borders. Its caterpillars, known as cutworms, eat grasses and other small plants.

WHEN ....

WHERE ....

Cutworm

Large yellow underwing

Garden tiger

Wingspan: 60–70mm (2¼–2¾in)

Garden tigers have orange back wings with black spots. Their front wings are mottled brown and cream. This moth's hairy caterpillar is called a woolly bear.

WHEN ....

WHERE ....

Silver Y

Silver Y

Wingspan: 40mm (1½in)

A silver Y is dull shades of brown with white markings on its front wings shaped like the letter "Y". It visits Europe from Africa in spring and summer, and often flies in daytime.

WHEN ....

WHERE ....

Cinnabar

Cinnabar

Wingspan: 40–45mm (1½–1¾in)

You might see this moth flying short distances by day. It has red back wings and dark brown front wings marked with two spots and two red streaks. Its yellow and black caterpillars feed on ragwort.

WHEN ....

WHERE ....

Hummingbird hawk-moth

Wingspan: 45mm (1¾in)

This moth hovers over flowers, beating its wings rapidly, like a hummingbird. It has brown front wings and orange back wings, and only flies during the day.

WHEN ....

WHERE ....

Hummingbird hawk-moth

Bees, wasps and ants

All the insects on this page live in big groups, called colonies, led by a large female called a queen.

Every honey bee has a job:

The females, called workers, do all the work.

One female, the queen, lays all the eggs.

The males, called drones, mate with the queen.

Buff-tailed bumblebee

Length: 22mm (¾in)

Often found around flowers, this bee has a big, furry, black and yellow body with a pale tan tip. The queen makes her nest in a hole in the ground.

WHEN ....

WHERE ....

Buff-tailed bumblebee

Honey bee

Length: 12–17mm (½–¾in)

Honey bees have golden brown bodies with black stripes towards their tail ends. People often keep colonies of honey bees in hives, to collect honey that they make.

WHEN ....

WHERE ....

Hornet

Hornet

Length: 22–30mm (¾–1¼in)

Hornets are very large wasps with brown and yellow markings on their rear parts.

WHEN ....

WHERE ....

Black ants   Winged males

Wingless female worker

Common wasp

Length: 15–20mm (½–¾in)

Wasp colonies often live inside a papery nest under ground. They are slimmer and less fuzzy than bees, and have clearer black and yellow stripes. Unlike bees, wasps sting to kill their prey.

WHEN ....

WHERE ....

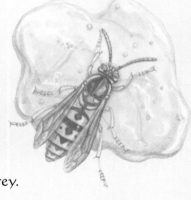

Common wasp

Black ant

Length: 3–9mm (⅛–¼in)

Male black ants have wings, and die after flying and mating. The queens are the only female ants with wings. They lose them after mating, then start new colonies of their own.

WHEN ....

WHERE ....

True flies and lacewings

True flies have two wings, while many other flying insects have four.

Common gnat

Giant cranefly or daddy-long-legs

Length: 30–40mm (1¼–1½in)

Often found near water, this large fly has a long, spindly body and very long legs. Its larvae, called leatherjackets, eat root crops and grass roots.

WHEN ....

WHERE ....

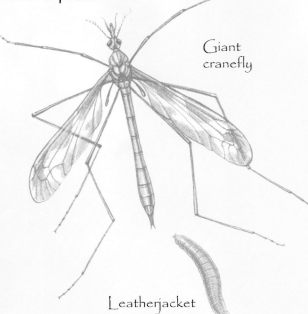

Giant cranefly

Leatherjacket

Common gnat or mosquito

Length: 6–7mm (about ¼in)

A common gnat is small, with a golden-brown body and very long, thin legs. The female sucks blood from people and animals.

WHEN ....

WHERE ....

Bluebottle

Bluebottle

Length: 9–15mm (¼–½in)

Also called blowflies, these hairy, blue flies are often heard buzzing loudly as they search for rotting meat on which to lay their eggs. Male bluebottles are most often seen lapping nectar from flowers.

WHEN ....

WHERE ....

Green lacewing

Green lacewing

Length: 15mm (½in)

Green lacewings have four wings covered with green, lace-like veins. You can find them mainly around gardens and hedges.

WHEN ....

WHERE ....

Hover fly

Length: 10–14mm (about ½in)

Hover fly

Hover flies look a bit like wasps, but do not sting. There are many types. This one is brown, with three light stripes on each side of its abdomen.

WHEN ....

WHERE ....

True bugs

True bugs are insects with sharp mouth-parts which they use for sucking the juices from plants or, in a few cases, from animals.

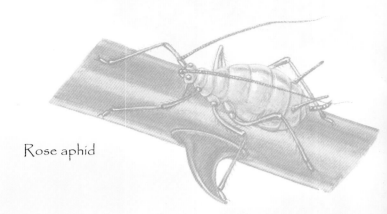

Rose aphid

Black bean aphid or blackfly

Length: 2–3mm (about ⅛in)

Broad beans and thistles often house large groups of these tiny, black bugs.

WHEN ....

WHERE ....

Black bean aphid

Green shieldbug

Rose aphid or greenfly

Length: 2–3mm (about ⅛in)

A rose aphid, or greenfly, is green or pinkish and shaped like a bulb. Its feelers are long compared to its body. This bug feeds on roses in the spring, making itself a pest. It produces a sweet, sticky syrup called honeydew, which ants eat.

WHEN ....

WHERE ....

Green shieldbug

Length: 12–14mm (about ½in)

You might find green shieldbugs on trees such as hazel and birch. They have a broad, green body with a light brown rear end.

WHEN ....

WHERE ....

Black and red froghopper

Length: 9–10mm (about ⅜in)

Like common froghoppers (below), these stripy bugs jump, and make "cuckoo spit". Their bold colours warn hungry animals that they taste nasty.

WHEN ....

WHERE ....

Common froghopper

Length: 6mm (¼in)

These pale green-brown bugs get their name from their amazing jumping skills. The young, called nymphs, live on plant stems, drinking their juice, and making a froth called cuckoo spit, in which they hide.

WHEN ....

WHERE ....

Common froghopper

Black and red froghopper

Beetles

There are more types of beetle than there are of any other creature on land. Here are just a few of the kinds you may find in a garden.

Seven-spot ladybird

Two-spot ladybird

Length: 4–6mm (about ¼in)

Most of these little beetles are red with two black spots, but the black marks may take other shapes, or they can even be black with four red spots. They eat aphids.

WHEN ....

WHERE ....

Two-spot ladybird

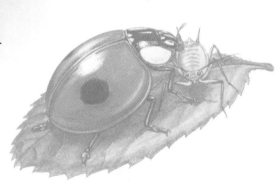

Seven-spot ladybird

Length: 6–8mm (about ¼in)

You're most likely to see these common ladybirds on sunny days. Their bright colours warn other animals that they don't taste good. If threatened, they release a foul-smelling yellow liquid. They spend the winter inside houses, sheds, or under tree bark.

WHEN ....

WHERE ....

Wasp beetle

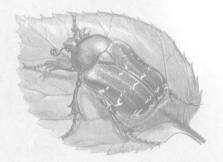

Rose chafer

Rose chafer

Length: 14–20mm (½–¾in)

A rose chafer's wing cases look almost square, but the front of its body is very round. This green beetle can be found all over Britain.

WHEN ....

WHERE ....

Cockchafer or maybug

Length: 25–30mm (1–1¼in)

You might see this beetle flying into lit windows in the early summer. It has a black head, brown wing cases, and is furry underneath.

WHEN ....

WHERE ....

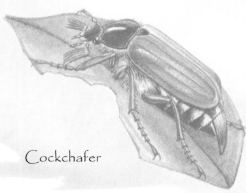

Cockchafer

Wasp beetle

Length: 15mm (½in)

This beetle looks like a wasp, with yellow stripes along its brown body. It flies around flowers on sunny days.

WHEN ....

WHERE ....

Devil's coach horse

Devil's coach horse or cocktail beetle

Length: 25–30mm (1–1¼in)

Often found in gardens, this black beetle can squirt its enemies with a foul-smelling liquid from its tail.

WHEN ....

WHERE ....

Violet ground beetle

Stag beetle

Length: 25–75mm (1–3in)

The largest beetles in Britain, male stag beetles have purplish wing cases, a black head and legs and long, antler-like jaws.

WHEN ....

WHERE ....

Stag beetle

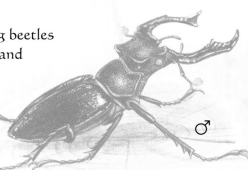
♂

Violet ground beetle

Length: 30–35mm (1¼–1½in)

Ground beetles spend a lot of time under the ground, but may be found underneath logs and stones in the garden. This ground beetle has a violet sheen to its black body. It eats worms, and other insects.

WHEN ....

WHERE ....

Click beetle or skip-jack

Length: 14–18mm (½–¾in)

If these beetles fall onto their backs they flip their bodies into the air with a loud click. There are many types: this one has a sleek, green body and branched feelers. Its larva is called a wireworm.

WHEN ....

WHERE ....

Click beetle

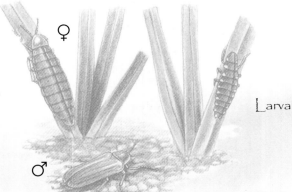
♀
Glow-worm
Larva
♂

Glow-worm

Male length: 15mm (½in)
Female length: 20mm (¾in)

Female glow-worms have long, brown bodies without wings or wing-cases. Their tails glow to attract males.

WHEN ....

WHERE ....

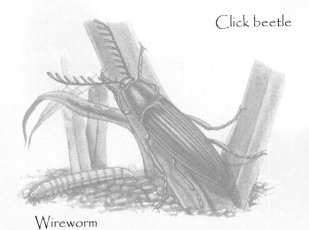
Wireworm

Pond life

Garden ponds attract a wide range of
living things, from insects that walk
on water to snakes that lurk beneath it.

Emperor
dragonfly

Pond skater

Length: 8–10mm (¼–½in)

Pond skaters are small, with very
long legs and thin bodies. They
skate with their middle legs, use
their back legs as rudders and
their front legs to catch prey.

WHEN ....

WHERE ....

Pond skater

Emperor dragonfly

Wingspan: 10.5cm (4in)

Often seen over garden ponds in summer,
this blue and green dragonfly is the largest
in Britain. It hunts butterflies and other
flying insects, catching them in mid-air.

WHEN ....

WHERE ....

Great pond snail

Length: 50mm (2in)

The biggest pond snail in Britain, this
creature has a long, spiralling shell,
and eats dead fish, newts and algae. It
is often seen floating upside-down on
the water's surface as it takes in air.

WHEN ....

WHERE ....

Great pond
snail

Water
spider

Water spider

Length: 10–15mm (about ½in)

This spider lives in an air-filled, underwater
web called a diving bell. As it swims, tiny
hairs on its body trap air, making it look
silvery. It preys on insect larvae, tadpoles
and small fish, and can give a painful bite.

WHEN ....

WHERE ....

Water
boatman

Water boatman
or backswimmer

Length: 15–20mm (½–¾in)

A water boatman's brown body is rather like
a little boat. It swims on its back, with the
tips of its legs clinging to the underside of
the water surface. Its back legs are shaped
like paddles and fringed with hairs.

WHEN ....

WHERE ....

Common frog

Length: up to 10cm (4in)

Common frogs have smooth, brown skin, which varies in shade, and black markings. They eat slugs, snails and insects. Frogs live mainly on land, but mate and lay eggs in water. Some males hibernate at the bottom of ponds.

WHEN ....

WHERE ....

Common frog

Frogspawn

Common toad

Length: up to 13cm (5in)

Toads only enter the water to breed. Their skin is warty and brownish, but changes shade, helping them to blend in with their surroundings. They hide by day, coming out at night to hunt slugs, snails, worms and insects.

WHEN ....

WHERE ....

Common toad

Toadspawn

Smooth newt

Length: 11cm (4¼in)

This common newt is brown with black spots, larger on the male. Males spend spring and early summer in water, trying to attract females by swishing their tails, wafting their body odour towards them. Before breeding, they grow a crest along their back and tail. The females enter the water to mate and lay eggs.

WHEN ....

WHERE ....

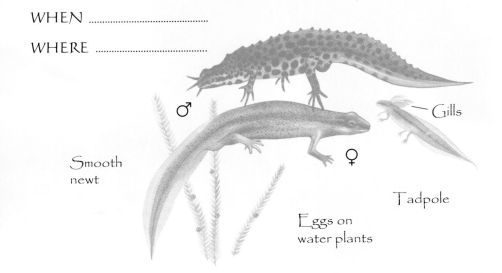

♂

♀

Gills

Smooth newt

Eggs on water plants

Tadpole

Spawn and tadpoles

Frogs and toads lay eggs, called spawn, which hatch into young called tadpoles. These look very different from their parents, and go through a series of body changes as they grow up.

WHEN ....

WHERE ....

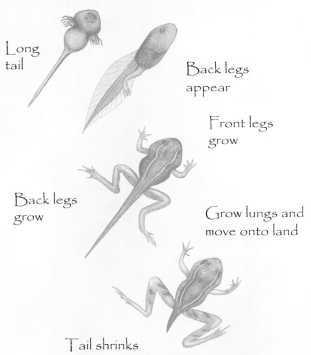

Long tail

Back legs appear

Front legs grow

Back legs grow

Grow lungs and move onto land

Tail shrinks

Grass snake

Length: Up to 120cm (47¼in)

These snakes aren't poisonous and are good swimmers, staying under water for a long time. They are brownish-green with a yellow "collar", edged in black. Grass snakes hunt frogs and toads, swallowing them alive.

WHEN ....

WHERE ....

Grass snake

Mammals

Many mammals visit gardens in the early morning, evening or night-time. To watch them, you'll have to be patient, and keep very still.

House mouse

House mouse

Length: 9cm (3½in)

House mice live near people, living off their scraps, as well as insects, grain and fruit. They have grey-brown fur and a tail as long as their body. Mice nest under floorboards, in sheds, or other hidey-holes. Each nest holds 4–8 naked young, which in just a month are fully-grown and able to have babies of their own.

WHEN ....

WHERE ....

Hedgehog

Length: 25cm (9¾in)

Easily recognized by their prickly spines, hedgehogs are usually seen at night, when they may travel a long distance, hunting for slugs and worms. When alarmed, they roll into a ball. They are often thought to be silent, but hedgehogs make many noises, including snuffles, snores and squeals.

WHEN ....

WHERE ....

Hedgehog

Brown rat

Length: 26cm (10¼in)

Brown rats are the world's most successful scavengers. They eat nearly anything – even soap. Rats live in large packs, making their home in buildings during winter, then moving in summer to sewers, canals and river banks.

WHEN ....

WHERE ....

Brown rat

Mole

Length: 13cm (5in)

Moles have velvety, black, tube-shaped bodies. They live under ground, digging tunnels with their strong front claws, and eating worms. Molehills, which sometimes appear on garden lawns, are the heaps of waste soil from their tunnels.

WHEN ....

WHERE ....

Common shrew

Length: 7cm (2¾in)

This small, fast-moving mammal lives in thick grass or bushes and eats worms and insects. It has a pointed, flexible snout and tiny eyes. Shrews sometimes nest in rubbish-heaps.

WHEN ....

WHERE ....

Common shrew

Mole

Grey squirrel

Length: 27cm (10¾in)

These acrobatic tree-dwellers are often seen in gardens, and will often go to great lengths to take nuts from bird-feeders. They build large nests, called dreys, from twigs and leaves, in the treetops.

WHEN ....

WHERE ....

Grey squirrel

Pipistrelle bat

Pipistrelle bat

Pipistrelle bat

Wingspan: 20–25cm (8–9¾in)

Often seen at dusk, as they catch insects on the wing, these small, brown bats fly in a jerky fashion. During the day, they rest in hollow trees or buildings.

WHEN ....

WHERE ....

Badger

Badger

Length: 75cm (30in)

With their black-and-white striped heads, badgers are hard to confuse with any other mammal. They spend the day under ground in burrow networks called setts, which are usually in wooded areas. At night they search for a wide range of foods, including worms, insects, grubs, nuts and berries. Some badgers raid bins for food.

WHEN ....

WHERE ....

Rabbit

Fox

Fox

Length: 67cm (26½in)

Nimble and rust-red, with white undersides and bushy tails, foxes are often seen in towns and gardens. They come out mainly at night, and often scavenge for food from bins. Male foxes are called dogs; females, vixens.

WHEN ....

WHERE ....

Rabbit

Length: 40cm (15¾in)

Rabbits live in groups in large, underground burrow networks, called warrens, often beneath grassy wasteland. Wild rabbits are usually brown-grey with pale bellies and white beneath their tails.

WHEN ....

WHERE ....

Index and checklist

This list will help you to find every animal in the book. The first number after each name tells you which page it is on. The second number (in brackets) is the number of its sticker.

Wildlife words

amphibian — A kind of soft-skinned animal that can live both on land and in water, lays soft eggs, and has a body temperature that changes with that of its surroundings

family — A group of similar, closely related animals, for example, the finch family, which includes chaffinches and siskins

gill — Part of the body that lets creatures breathe under water

hibernation — Sleeping or resting through the winter

insect — A kind of animal with six legs and a body divided into three main parts. Most have wings.

larva — A stage in some insects' young lives when they look very different from their parents

mammal — A kind of animal that is usually hairy, feeds its babies with milk, and has a constant body temperature

nocturnal — Active mainly at night

Front cover © blickwinkel/Alamy; Back cover © 2006 Topfoto/Profimedia
Cover design: Michael Hill; Digital imaging: Keith Furnival

Additional illustrators: Joyce Bee, John Barber, Hilary Burn, Tim Hayward, Ian Jackson, Aziz Khan, Rachel Lockwood, Alan Male, Andy Martin, Annabel Milne, Dee Morgan, David Palmer, Julie Piper, Chris Shields, Peter Stebbing, Josephine Martin, David Wright

First published in 2007 by Usborne Publishing Ltd., 83–85 Saffron Hill, London EC1N 8RT, England. Copyright © 2007 Usborne Publishing Ltd.